chloe and co

chloe and co

by Gray & Shack

It's the bad girls from the **Daily Mail**

hamlyn

An Hachette UK Company
www.hachette.co.uk

Hamlyn, a division of Octopus Publishing Group Ltd
Endeavour House
189 Shaftesbury Avenue
London
WC2H 8JY
www.octopusbooks.co.uk

ISBN 978-0-600-62118-8

A CIP catalogue record for this book is available from the British Library

Printed and bound in China

2 4 6 8 10 9 7 5 3 1

The cartoons are distributed by Knight Features Limited

The Daily Mail name and logo are registered trade marks of Associated
Newspapers Limited

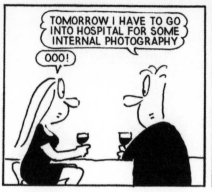

WHAT KIND OF DRESS IS THAT?

THE KIND OF DRESS GEORGE WILL LIKE

TEN PERCENT COTTON, NINETY PERCENT ME

POOR MARCE HAS BEEN IN HOSPITAL OVER EASTER

OH NO! I'LL SEND HER SOME FLOWERS

WHAT'S SHE GOT?

ROSES MAINLY, AND SOME TULIPS. A BUNCH OF DAFFS MIGHT BE NICE

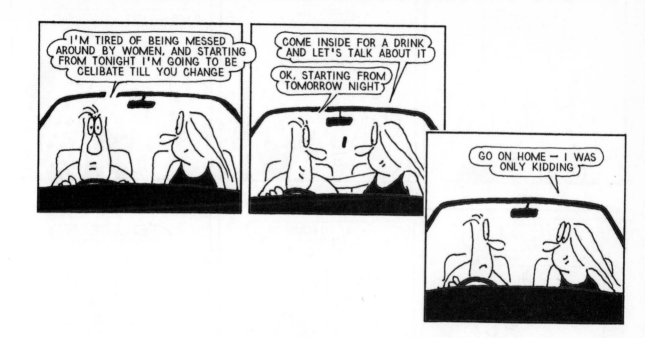